A Spring Thing

A Spring Thing

Words and Music by
Matthew Crossey

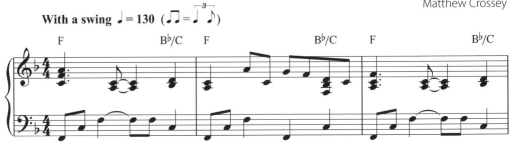

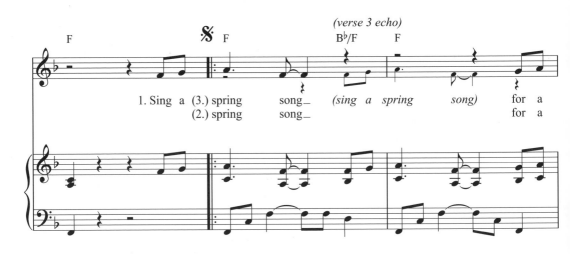

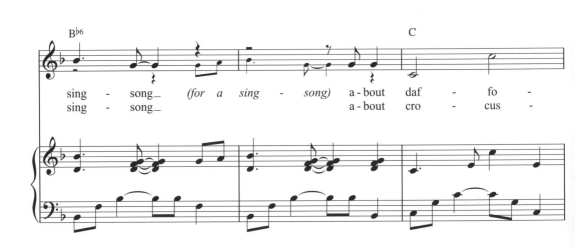

- dils and snow - drops, and if we
- es and blue - bells, and if we

all sing,_ (and if we all sing) this lit - tle spring thing (this lit - tle
all sing,_ this lit - tle spring thing

To Coda ⊕

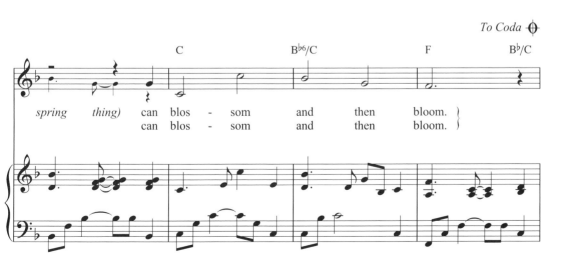

spring thing) can blos - som and then bloom.)
can blos - som and then bloom.)

3

Sing_____ this song_with all_ your_____ heart,

as win - - ter ends_ be-fore sum-mer_____

_____ starts._ 2. Sing a 3. Sing a

4

CODA

thing.

all *sing)* this lit - tle spring thing *(this lit - tle spring thing)* can

blos - som and then bloom, can

blos - som and then bloom.

A Tiny Seed Was Sleeping

Words and Music by
Niki Davies

With a gentle lilt ♩. = 52

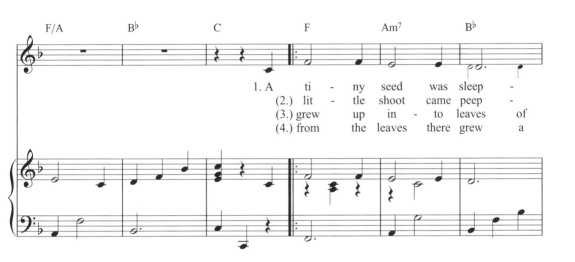

1. A ti – ny seed was sleep –
(2.) lit – tle shoot came peep –
(3.) grew up in – to leaves of
(4.) from the leaves there grew a

– ing un – der – neath the ground. A ti – ny
– ing out of the seed. A lit – tle
green, sway – ing in the breeze. It grew up
flower, yel – low and bright. And from the

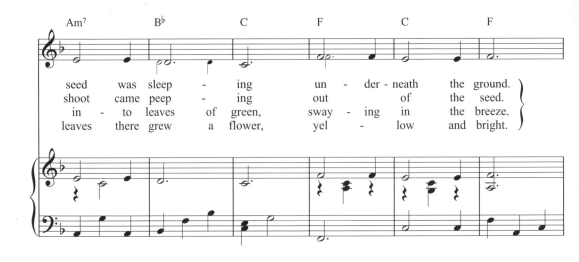

seed was sleep - ing un - der - neath the ground.
shoot came peep - ing out of the seed.
in - to leaves of green, sway - ing in the breeze.
leaves there grew a flower, yel - low and bright.

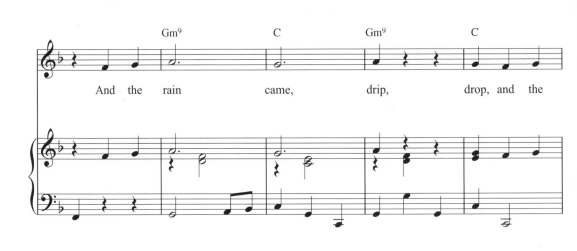

And the rain came, drip, drop, and the

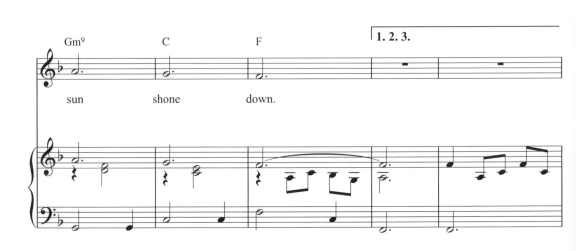

1. 2. 3.

sun shone down.

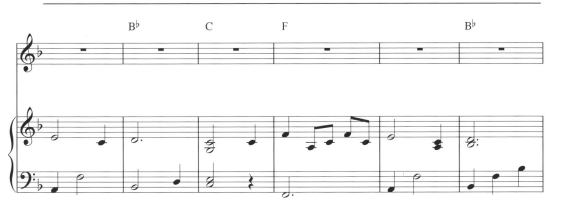

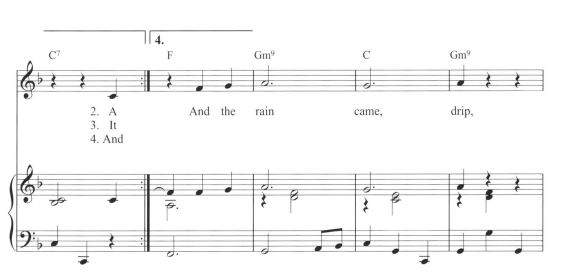

2. A　　　　　And the rain　came,　drip,
3. It
4. And

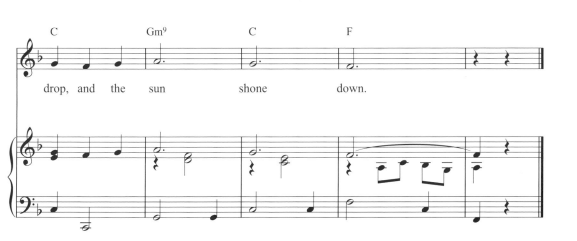

drop, and the　sun　shone　down.

CAN YOU HEAR THE DONKEY?

Words and Music by
Mary Green and Julie Stanley

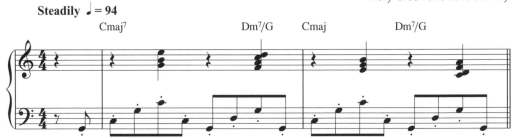

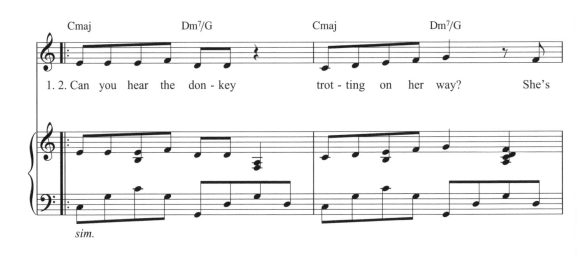

1. 2. Can you hear the don - key trot - ting on her way? She's

go - ing to Je - ru - sa - lem this ve - ry spe - cial day.

Can you hear the chil-dren trot-ting by her side

as she gives King Je-sus this ve-ry spe-cial ride? Ho-

-san-na to King Je-sus, ho-san-na to the King,

wave your bran-ches, raise your voi-ces, dance a-long and sing. Ho-

EASTER PRAYER

Words and Music by
Mary Green and Julie Stanley

With feeling ♩ = 74

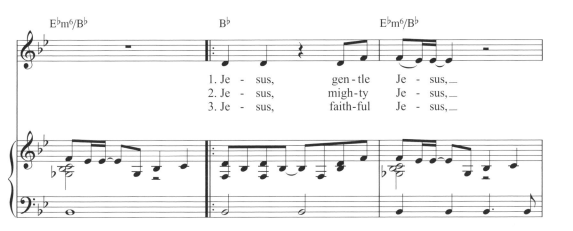

1. Je - sus, gen - tle Je - sus,__
2. Je - sus, migh - ty Je - sus,__
3. Je - sus, faith - ful Je - sus,__

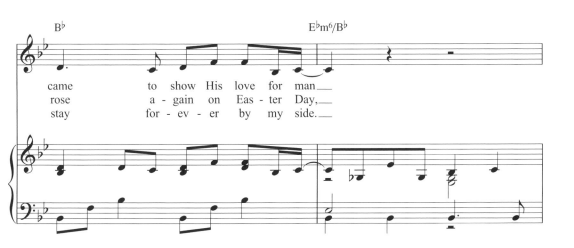

came to show His love for man__
rose a - gain on Eas - ter Day,__
stay for - ev - er by my side.__

love .... so great He e - ven died for us, ___
showed ...... His po - wer and for - give - ness, ___
Stay .... and help me serve you faith - ful - ly, ___

with His death new life be - gan. ___
made us free to live His way. ___
be my friend and be my guide. ___

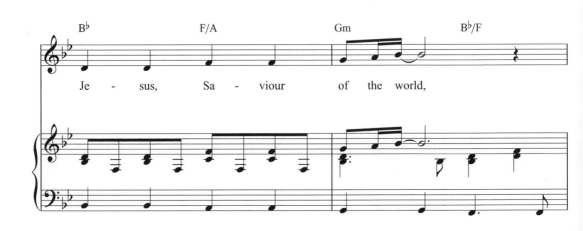

Je - sus, Sa - viour of the world,

14

walk be - side us ev - ery day,

walk be - side us now, we pray.

walk be - side us now, we pray.

CELEBRATE

Words and Music by
Mark and Helen Johnson

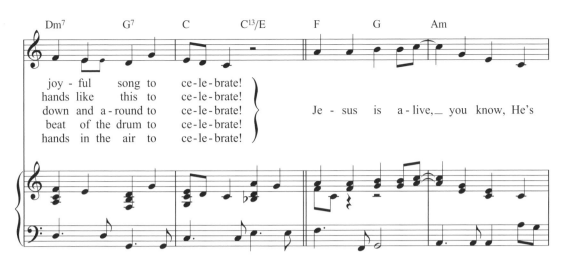

joy - ful song to ce - le - brate!
hands like this to ce - le - brate!
down and a - round to ce - le - brate!
beat of the drum to ce - le - brate!
hands in the air to ce - le - brate!

Je - sus is a - live,_ you know, He's

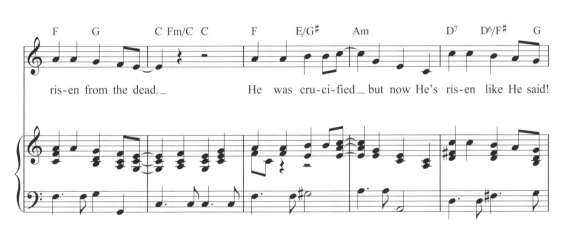

ris - en from the dead._

He was cru - ci - fied_ but now He's ris - en like He said!

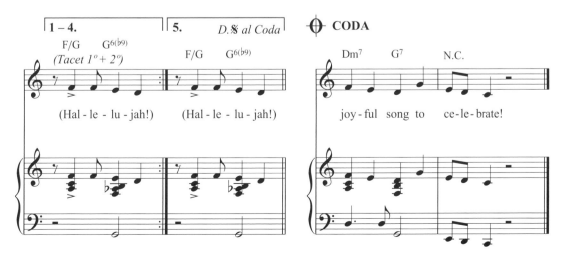

1 – 4.

(Tacet 1° + 2°)

(Hal - le - lu - jah!)

5. *D. % al Coda*

(Hal - le - lu - jah!)

⊕ **CODA**

joy - ful song to ce - le - brate!

HALLELUJAH!

Words and Music by
Mark and Helen Johnson

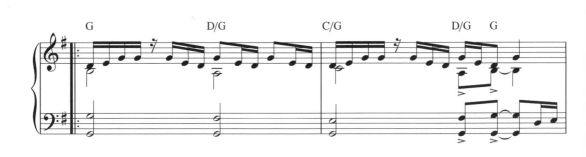

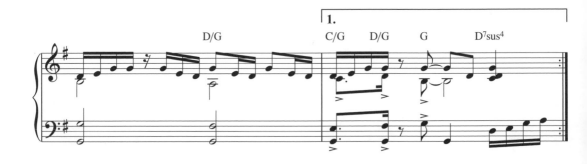

Hal - le - lu - jah! Je-sus Christ is a-ris-en.

Hal - le - lu - jah! Je-sus is__ a-live. Hal - le - lu - jah!

To Coda

Je-sus Christ is a-ris-en. Hal - le - lu - jah! Je-sus is__ a-live.__

1. There's a sto - ry that must be told,
2. Je - sus died__ on a cross, we know,

there's a mes - sage that we've been giv - en.
ev - ery breath that He had was giv - en.

There's a Sa - viour for us to know,
Break-ing the power of death, He rose!

1. love has con - quered, Je - sus__ is ris - en!
King for - ev - er,

2. *D.% al Coda* Je - sus__ has ris - en!

HAY FEVER

Words and Music by
Paul Field

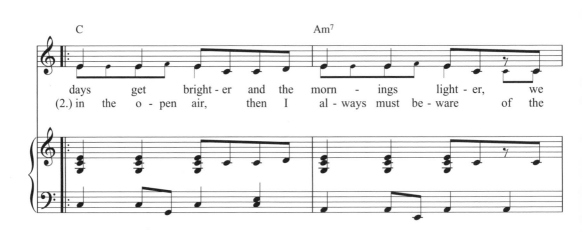

birds   are   sing - ing   and   the   blue - bells   ring - ing,   we
lawn   needs   mow - ing   then   I   know   I   must   be   go - ing   to

know   spring   is   knock - ing   at   the   door.   But   it's
take   a   dose   of   an - ti - his - ta - mine.   You   see   it's

not   so   good   for   me   'cos   I've   got   an   al - ler - gy   to
not   so   good   for   me   'cos   I've   got   an   al - ler - gy   to

pol - len   car - ried   on   the   breeze,___   and   the
pol - len   car - ried   on   the   breeze,___   and   the

HEY LITTLE APRIL SHOWER

Words and Music by
Niki Davies

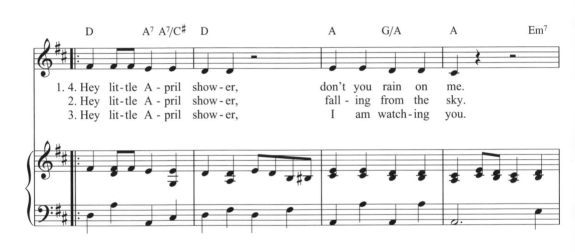

1. 4. Hey lit-tle A-pril show-er,   don't you rain on me.
2. Hey lit-tle A-pril show-er,   fall-ing from the sky.
3. Hey lit-tle A-pril show-er,   I am watch-ing you.

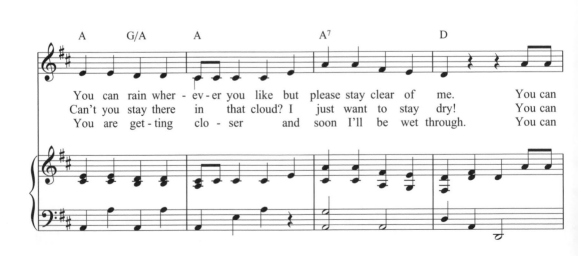

You can rain wher-ev-er you like but please stay clear of me. You can
Can't you stay there in that cloud? I just want to stay dry! You can
You are get-ting clo-ser and soon I'll be wet through. You can

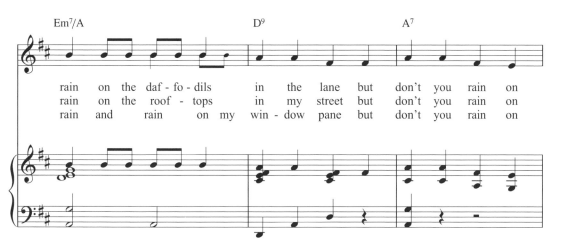

rain on the daf-fo-dils in the lane but don't you rain on
rain on the roof-tops in my street but don't you rain on
rain and rain on my win-dow pane but don't you rain on

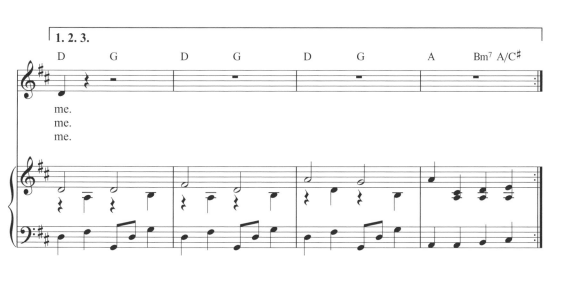

1. 2. 3.

me.
me.
me.

4.

me.

HIP, HIP, HOORAY!
(WE'RE HAVING A HOLIDAY)

Words and Music by
Mark and Helen Johnson

1. We've been work-ing ve-ry hard eve-ry day,
2. No more nag-ging to be rea-dy on time,
3. No more les-sons for a cou-ple of weeks,
4. Say 'Good-bye' to all your teach-ers and friends,

we're all rea-dy for a rest. *[Teachers: A-men!]* Now's the time to have a
no more rush-ing out of bed. No more 'Wa-key, wa-key!
no more home-work for a while. *[Yee hah!]* Won't be long till we can
please re-mem-ber all you've learned. Take good care un-til we

* 'Easter time' can be substituted with 'Christmas time' or 'end of term' as appropriate.

HOSANNA

Words and Music by
Mark and Helen Johnson

Punchy and positive ♩ = 162

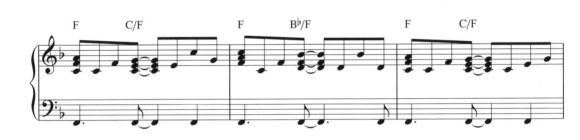

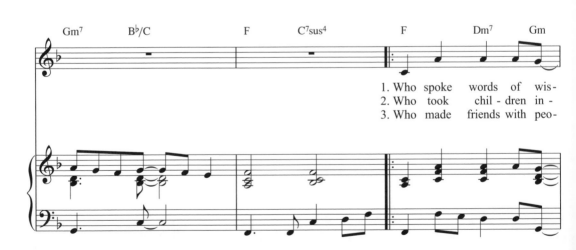

1. Who spoke words of wis-
2. Who took chil - dren in -
3. Who made friends with peo-

CCLI Song No. 1574833

- dom and life? *On - ly the one __ they call Je - sus.*
- to his arms? *On - ly the one __ they call Je - sus.*
- ple des - pised? *On - ly the one __ they call Je - sus.*

Un - der - stood what peo - ple are like? *No - bo - dy o - ther than*
Spoke to storms and made __ them be calm? *No - bo - dy o - ther than*
Turned the wa - ter in - to good wine? *No - bo - dy o - ther than*

Him. Who per - formed mi - ra - cu - lous signs?
Him. Who raised Laz - 'rus up __ from the dead?
Him. Who got peo - ple fol - low-ing him?

Lyrics:

Verse lines (stanzas 1–3):
On - ly the one__ they call Je - sus. Healed the sick, gave sight__
On - ly the one__ they call Je - sus. Made a feast of fish -
On - ly the one__ they call Je - sus. Changed their lives, for - gave__

____ to the blind? No - bo - dy o - ther than Him.
- es and bread? No - bo - dy o - ther than Him.
____ all their sin? No - bo - dy o - ther than Him.

Group 2: Re -
Group 1: Ho -

- joice!_____ Sing praise!_____
- san - na!__ Ho - san - na!__ Praise Him,__ come

33

MARCH, APRIL, MAY

Words and Music by
Mary Green and Julie Stanley

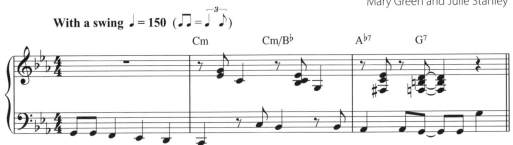

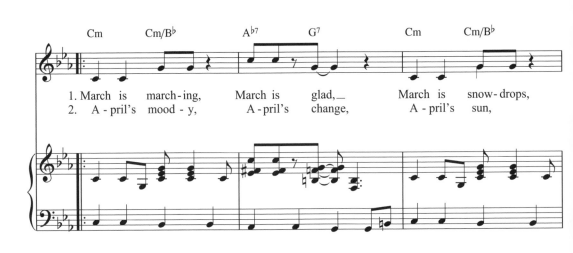

1. March is march-ing, March is glad,__ March is snow-drops,
2. A - pril's mood - y, A - pril's change, A - pril's sun,

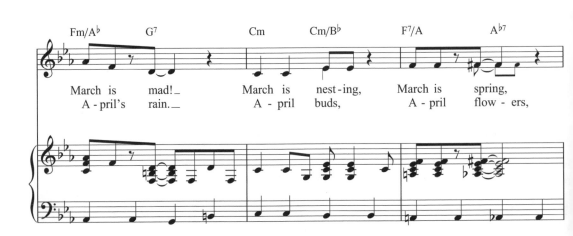

March is mad!__ March is nest-ing, March is spring,
A - pril's rain.__ A - pril buds, A - pril flow - ers,

March shouts, 'Wake up ev-ery - thing!'
A - pril sings in A - pril show - ers!

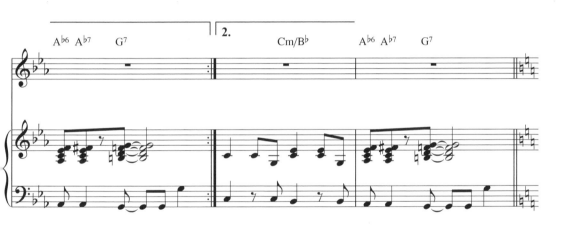

3. May is joy-ful, May is bright! May is blos-som,

May is white. May is fun, May is play,__

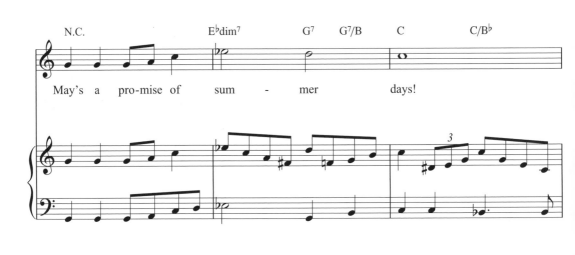

May's a pro-mise of sum - mer days!

MAY DAY DANCE

Words and Music by
Jeff Hammer

My Mum

Words and Music by
Mark and Helen Johnson

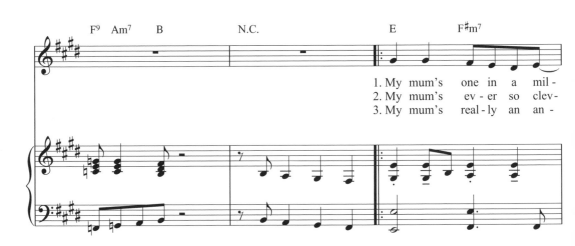

1. My mum's one in a mil -
2. My mum's ev - er so clev -
3. My mum's real - ly an an -

- lion,   I'm sure that you would a - gree.
- er,   she may not have a de - gree,
- gel,   she's great at car - ing for me.

I would-n't say that she's per - fect, but
but she can help with my home - work and
She does the clean-ing and shop - ping and

she's the best one for me.
that's what mat-ters to me.
makes a won-der-ful tea!

Some - times she can get grum-
Some - times she can be stres-
Some - times she is too bu -

- py, and some - times she gets up - set, but
- sy, some - times e - ven she shouts! But
- sy, some - times she is worn out, but

I still know that she loves___ me, and that I'll nev-er for-get!
I still know that she loves___ me, and that's what cer-tain-ly counts!
I still know that she loves___ me, and that's what this is a-bout!

Oh! This is a Mo-ther's Day song for you. Mum,_____ you're ev-er so spe-cial and I'm gon-na find ways_ to say I love you too!

NEW BEGINNINGS

Words and Music by
Sha Armstrong

Steadily ♩ = 130

Lyrics:

It's time for new be-gin-nings when cold dark days are at an end,_ it's time for new be-gin-nings when spring is in the air and hope is ev-ery-where, then it's

To Coda

CCLI Song No. 5280779

CODA

time to live a - gain,___ live a - gain,___

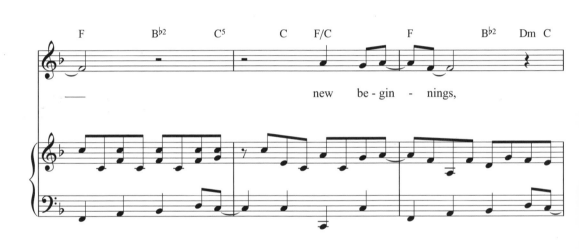

___ new be - gin - nings,

new be - gin - nings.

Spring Chicken

Words and Music by
Mark and Helen Johnson

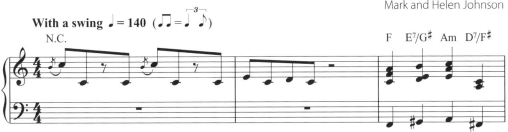

1. One mo-ther hen sat on **four** lit-tle eggs,
2. One mo-ther hen sat on **three** lit-tle eggs,
3. One mo-ther hen sat on **two** lit-tle eggs,
4. One mo-ther hen sat on **one** lit-tle egg,

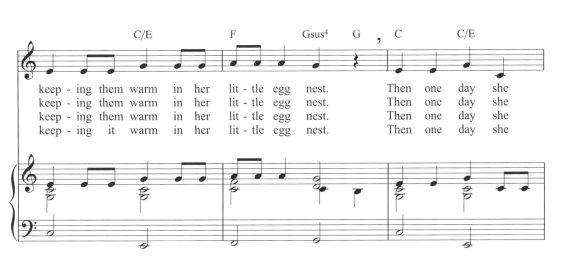

keep-ing them warm in her lit-tle egg nest. Then one day she
keep-ing them warm in her lit-tle egg nest. Then one day she
keep-ing them warm in her lit-tle egg nest. Then one day she
keep-ing it warm in her lit-tle egg nest. Then one day she

PANCAKES

Words and Music by
Mark and Helen Johnson

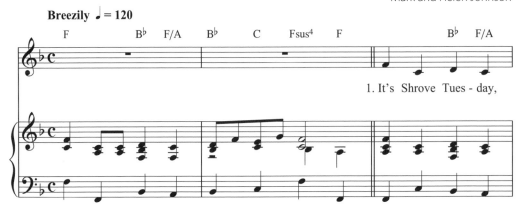

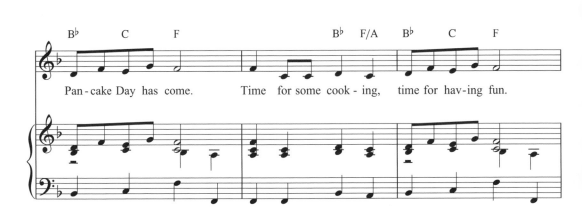

Pan - cake Day has come.   Time for some cook - ing,   time for hav - ing fun.

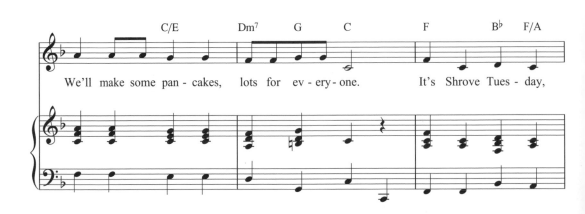

We'll make some pan - cakes,   lots for ev - ery - one.   It's Shrove Tues - day,

CCLI Song No. 1092982

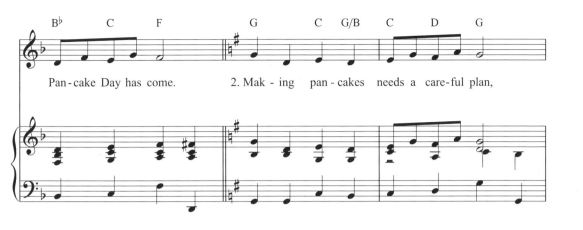

Pan-cake Day has come. 2. Mak-ing pan-cakes needs a care-ful plan,

eggs, milk and flour,__ but-ter and a pan. 'Bet-ter roll your sleeves up,

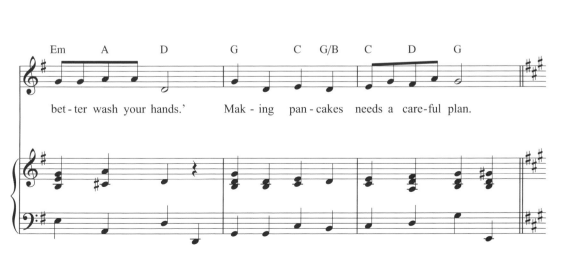

bet-ter wash your hands.' Mak-ing pan-cakes needs a care-ful plan.

3. For the mix - ture this is what you do: blend the in - gre - di - ents

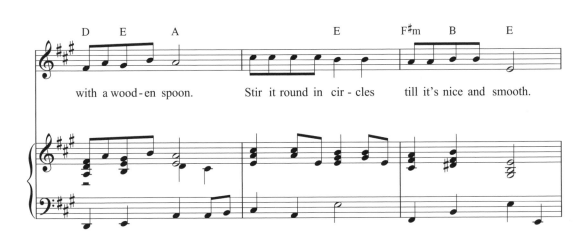

with a wood - en spoon. Stir it round in cir - cles till it's nice and smooth.

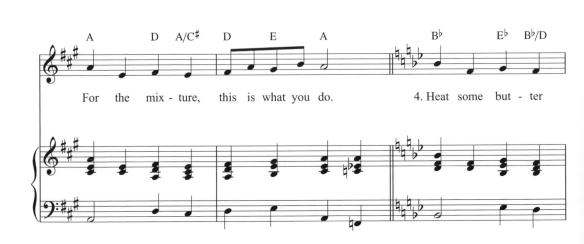

For the mix - ture, this is what you do. 4. Heat some but - ter

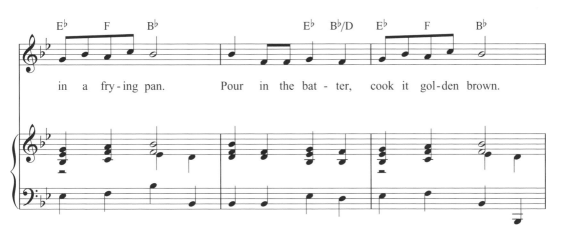

in a fry-ing pan. Pour in the bat - ter, cook it gol-den brown.

Give the pan a jig - gle, shake it all a-round. Now toss the pan - cake,...

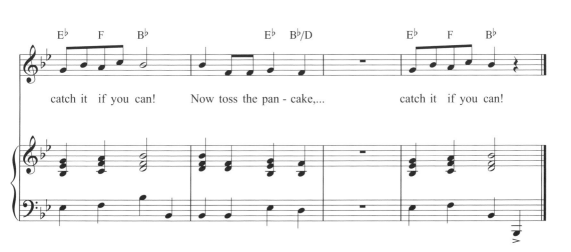

catch it if you can! Now toss the pan - cake,... catch it if you can!

SING OUT AN EASTER SONG

Words and Music by
Mark and Helen Johnson

Sing out_ an Eas-ter song, tell ev-ery-one_ that the Lord has ris-en.

Sing out_ a joy-ful song, tell ev-ery-bo-dy that He's a-live!

SPRING IN MY TOES

Words and Music by
Niki Davies

1. 2. 3. 5. I've got a spring, spring,
(4. *Instrumental*)

spring in my toes,___ I've got a spring, spring,

57

Spring Into Action

Words and Music by
Sha Armstrong

Spring in - to ac - tion – win - ter has gone, __ spring in - to ac - tion –

sum - mer come on, __ the days are get - ting long - er, the light is get - ting strong - er,

spring in - to ac - tion now.

1. To - day it's time to   sow the   seeds
2. To - day it's time to   clean the   house
3. To - day it's time to   play out - side __

now that spring is here, ___ to - day it's time to sow the seeds, it's my
now that spring is here, ___ to - day it's time to clean the house, it's my
now that spring is here, ___ to - day it's time to play out - side, ___ it's my

1. 2. **3.** *D.% al Coda*

fav - ourite sea - son of the year...
fav - ourite sea - son of the year...
fav - ourite sea - son of the year...

CODA

spring in - to ac - tion now, spring in - to ac - tion now.

SPRING FEVER!

Words and Music by
Mary Green and Julie Stanley

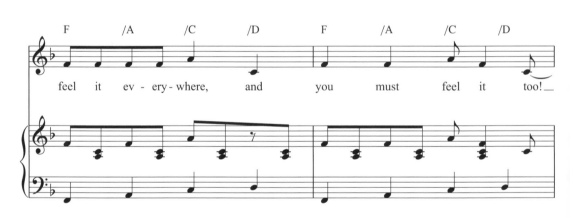

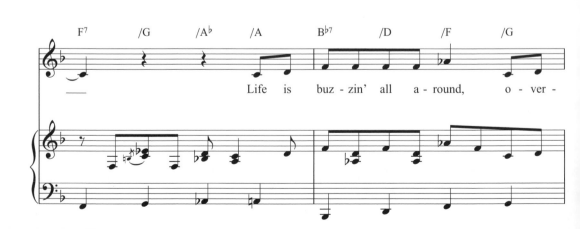

CCLI Song No. 5280786

SUNSHINE, SHOWERS AND RAINBOWS

Words and Music by
Matthew Crossey

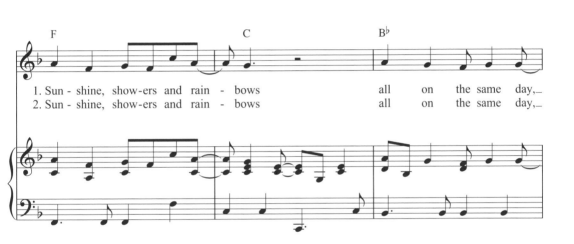

1. Sun - shine, show-ers and rain - bows all on the same day,_
2. Sun - shine, show-ers and rain - bows all on the same day,_

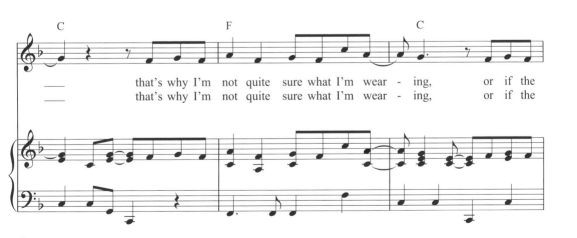

that's why I'm not quite sure what I'm wear - ing, or if the
that's why I'm not quite sure what I'm wear - ing, or if the

CCLI Song No. 5280803

rain is here to stay.___ It could be Wel-ling-ton boots, a
sun is here to stay.___ It could be sun-hat and shorts, a

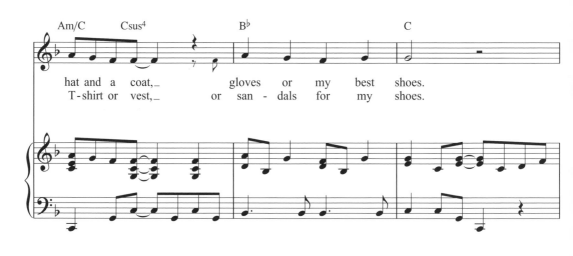

hat and a coat,_ gloves or my best shoes.
T-shirt or vest,_ or san - dals for my shoes.

Sun - shine, show-ers and rain - bows, that's why I don't know what to
Sun - shine, show-ers and rain - bows, that's why I don't know what to

THE APRIL SHOWERS

Words and Music by
Sha Armstrong

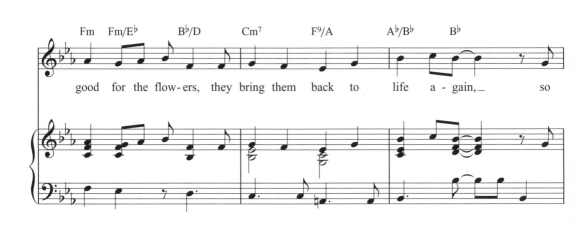

The Chocolate Song

Words and Music by
Mark and Helen Johnson

With a 'country' feel ♩ = 126

Oh I've got lots of choc-olate, give me

love - ly choc-olate, it's the best thing to eat, for sure. When I get

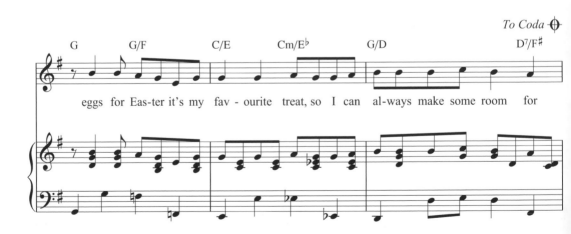

eggs for Eas-ter it's my fav - ourite treat, so I can al-ways make some room for

more!

1. I've got some plain and milk ones and some tof‑fee‑filled ones, I've got
2. I've ea‑ten milk‑y white ones and the sweets in‑side them, (I've got
3. I've had some sick‑ly sweet ones and some pret‑ty cheap ones, but I

box‑es all a‑round the place. I've got a strong af‑fec‑tion for my
choc‑olate all a‑round my face!) They all had pret‑ty wrap‑pers, but that's
could‑n't see them go to waste. I s'pose I should know bet‑ter, but it's

1. 2.

choc‑olate col‑lec‑tion, I'm mad a‑bout that choc‑olate taste!)
not what mat‑ters, I'm mad a‑bout that choc‑olate taste!)
near‑ly Eas‑ter, I'm mad a‑bout that choc‑olate

Oh I've got

69

SUPERMUM!

Words and Music by
Ann Beresford

hold three con-ver-sa-tions whilst do-ing my sums, she's a re-gu-lar Su - per - mum, (oh yeah), she's a won-der-ful Su - per - mum! Yes she's a great, fan-tas-tic, love e-las-tic Su - per-mum, she's a

THE POT OF CRESS

Words and Music by
Mary Green and Julie Stanley

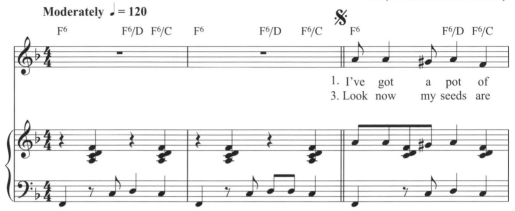

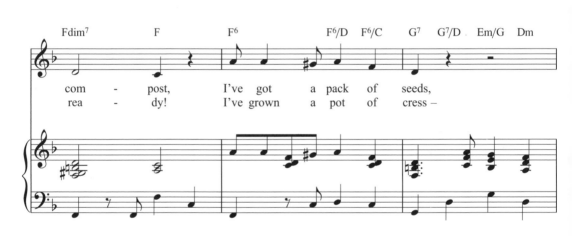

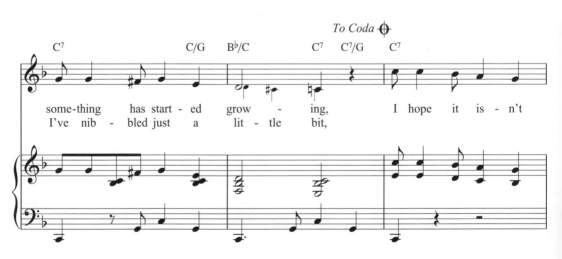

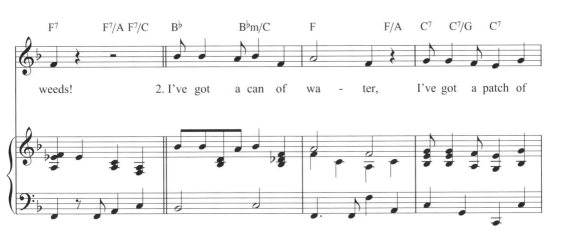

weeds! 2. I've got a can of wa - ter, I've got a patch of

sun, the shoots are get - ting tal - ler and I've mea - sured ev - ery

CODA

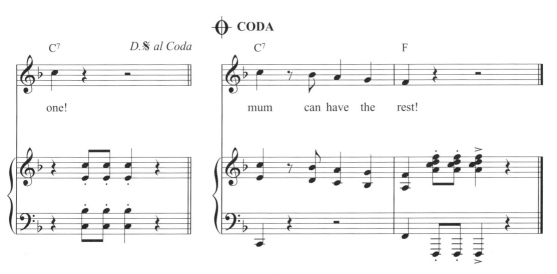

one! *D.% al Coda*

mum can have the rest!

75

The Season of Singing

Words and Music by
Mark and Helen Johnson

1. It's quite a thing___

when the win - ter turns to spring, when the earth___

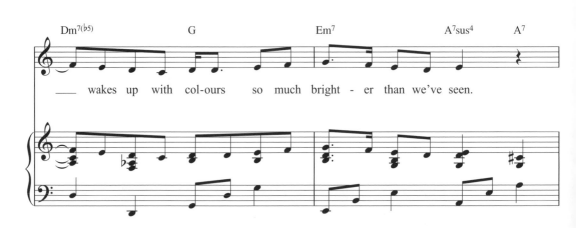

___ wakes up with col-ours so much bright - er than we've seen.

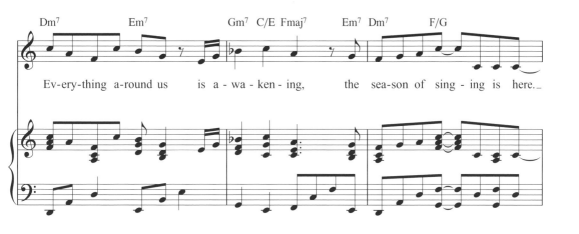

Ev-ery-thing a-round us   is a - wa - ken - ing,   the sea-son of sing - ing is here.

2. It's quite a thing (4.) when you
   (3.) when the

hear the call of spring,   when the birds sit in the tree - tops and the
win - ter turns to spring,   when the earth wakes up with col-ours   so much

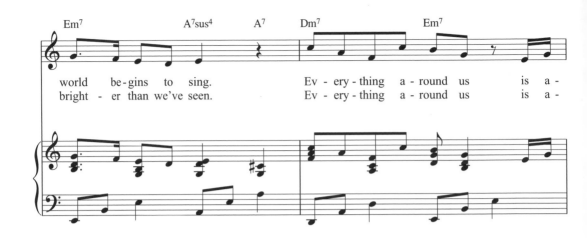

world be-gins to sing. Ev - ery-thing a - round us is a -
bright - er than we've seen. Ev - ery-thing a - round us is a -

To Coda

-wa - ken - ing, the sea-son of sing - ing is here.
-wa - ken - ing, the sea-son of sing - ing is here.

Harmony 2° only

Win - ter is gone, there's a warmth in the sun, there's a fra -

78

The Signs of the Time

Words and Music by
Mary Green and Julie Stanley

1. The sun is in the sky and the clouds are float-ing high, now the
(2.) daf-fo-dils are bright and the ti-ny lambs are white, now the

black-bird has built her nest. The trees are turn-ing green and there's
ro-bin has built her nest. The hedge-hog's a-wake and the

blos-som to be seen, now the world is___ at it's best —
duck has found her drake, now the world is___ at it's best —

these are the signs, the signs of the time, and the time is—

1.

spring.   2. The

2.   *poco rit.*

spring.   These are the signs, the signs of the time, and the time is—

a tempo   *rit.*

spring.

TICK TOCK
(THE CLOCKS GO FORWARD)

Words and Music by
Mark and Helen Johnson

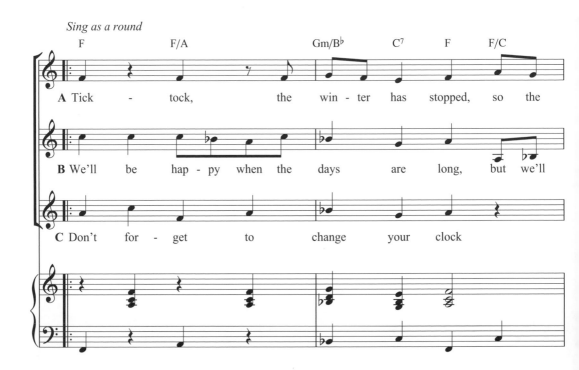

WAKE UP!

Words and Music by
Mark and Helen Johnson

Lyrics:

1-4. Wake up! Wake up! Give your-self a shake up,

§ Instrumental

get your bo-dy mov - ing. Reach up, jump up,

1. 3.

give your friend the 'thumbs up'! It's an-o-ther new day!

WE'VE BEEN WAITING

Words and Music by
Nikki Lewis

Animated ♩ = 140

We've been wait-ing all through the win-ter, we've been wait-ing to say, 'No time to wait, to-day's the date, it's too late to hi-ber-nate, get out of your bed, you

A Spring Thing

Words and Music by Matthew Crossey

1   Sing a spring song
For a sing-song
About daffodils and snowdrops,
And if we all sing,
This little spring thing
Can blossom and then bloom.

Sing this song with all your heart,
As winter ends before summer starts.

2   Sing a spring song
For a sing-song
About crocuses and bluebells,
And if we all sing,
This little spring thing,
Can blossom and then bloom.

Sing this song with all your heart,
As winter ends before summer starts.

GROUP 1	GROUP 2
3 Sing a spring song,	*Sing a spring song,*
For a sing-song,	*For a sing-song.*
About daffodils and snowdrops,	
And if we all sing,	*And if we all sing,*
This little spring thing	*This little spring thing)*
Can blossom and then bloom.	

GROUP 1	GROUP 2	GROUP 3
4 Sing a spring song,	*Sing a spring song,*	*Song,*
For a sing-song,	*For a sing-song.*	*Song.*
About crocuses and bluebells,		
And if we all sing,	*And if we all sing,*	*Sing,*
This little spring thing,	*This little spring thing.*	*Thing.*
Can blossom and then bloom,		
Can blossom and then bloom.		

A Tiny Seed Was Sleeping

Words and Music by Niki Davies

1 A tiny seed was sleeping underneath the ground.
A tiny seed was sleeping underneath the ground.
And the rain came, drip, drop,
And the sun shone down.

2 A little shoot came peeping out of the seed.
A little shoot came peeping out of the seed.
And the rain came, drip, drop,
And the sun shone down.

3 It grew up into leaves of green, swaying in the breeze.
It grew up into leaves of green, swaying in the breeze.
And the rain came, drip, drop,
And the sun shone down.

4 And from the leaves there grew a flower, yellow and bright.
And from the leaves there grew a flower, yellow and bright.
And the rain came, drip, drop,
And the sun shone down.

And the rain came, drip, drop,
And the sun shone down.

Can You Hear The Donkey?

Words and Music by Mary Green and Julie Stanley

1   Can you hear the donkey
    Trotting on her way?
    She's going to Jerusalem
    This very special day.
    Can you hear the children
    Trotting by her side
    As she gives King Jesus
    This very special ride?

   CHORUS   *Hosanna to King Jesus,*
             Hosanna to the King,
             Wave your branches, raise your voices,
             Dance along and sing.
             Hosanna to King Jesus,
             Hosanna to the King,
             Lay your coat to make a path
             Of welcome for the King.

2   Can you hear the donkey
    Trotting on her way?
    She's going to Jerusalem
    This very special day.
    Can you hear the children
    Trotting by her side
    As she gives King Jesus
    This very special ride?

   CHORUS x 2

   Eee-aww!

CELEBRATE

Words and Music by Mark and Helen Johnson

1   Sing a song, sing a joyful song,
Sing a joyful song to celebrate!
(Repeat)

    CHORUS   *Jesus is alive, you know,*
He's risen from the dead.
He was crucified but now He's
Risen like He said! (Hallelujah!)

2   Clap your hands, clap your hands like this,
Clap your hands like this to celebrate!
(Repeat)

    CHORUS

3   Jump up and down, up and down and around,
Up and down and around to celebrate!
(Repeat)

    CHORUS

4   Dance to the beat, to the beat of the drum,
To the beat of the drum to celebrate!
(Repeat)

    CHORUS

5   Wave your hands, wave your hands in the air,
Wave your hands in the air to celebrate!
(Repeat)

    CHORUS

6   Sing a song, sing a joyful song,
Sing a joyful song to celebrate!
(Repeat)

EASTER PRAYER

Words and Music by Mary Green and Julie Stanley

1 Jesus, gentle Jesus,
   Came to show His love for man –
   Love so great He even died for us,
   With His death new life began.

   CHORUS   *Jesus, Saviour of the world,*
   Walk beside us every day,
   Walk beside us now, we pray.

2 Jesus, mighty Jesus,
   Rose again on Easter Day,
   Showed His power and forgiveness
   Made us free to live His way.

   CHORUS

3 Jesus, faithful Jesus,
   Stay forever by my side.
   Stay and help me serve you faithfully,
   Be my friend and be my guide.

   CHORUS

CCLI Song No. 5280717

HALLELUJAH!

Words and Music by Mark and Helen Johnson

CHORUS   *Hallelujah! Jesus Christ is a-risen.*
Hallelujah! Jesus is alive.
Hallelujah! Jesus Christ is a-risen.
Hallelujah! Jesus is alive.

1   There's a story that must be told,
There's a message that we've been given.
There's a Saviour for us to know,
Love has conquered, Jesus is risen!

CHORUS

2   Jesus died on a cross, we know,
Every breath that He had was given.
Breaking the power of death, He rose!
King forever, Jesus has risen!

CHORUS x 3

HAY FEVER

Words and Music by Paul Field

1   When the days get brighter and the mornings lighter,
    We don't need winter woollies anymore.
    When the birds are singing and the bluebells ringing,
    We know spring is knocking at the door.
    But it's not so good for me 'cos I've got an allergy
    To pollen carried on the breeze,
    And the sunshine you're enjoying can be really quite annoying,
    It makes me want to sneeze.

CHORUS   *Here comes that hay, hay fever,*
         With the runny nose and itchy eyes.
         Here comes that hay, hay fever,
         Maybe you don't realize.
         When spring is sprung and the flowers have come
         It's great for the birds and bees,
         But that old hay, hay fever
         Just makes me want to… (achoo!)

2   So when I'm in the open air, then I always must beware
    Of the flowers or anything that's green,
    And when the lawn needs mowing then I know I must be going
    To take a dose of antihistamine.
    You see it's not so good for me 'cos I've got an allergy
    To pollen carried on the breeze,
    And the sunshine you're enjoying can be really quite annoying,
    It makes me want to sneeze.

CHORUS x 2

(Lots of sneezing!)

HEY LITTLE APRIL SHOWER

Words and Music by Niki Davies

1 Hey little April shower,
  Don't you rain on me.
  You can rain wherever you like
  But please stay clear of me.
  You can rain on the daffodils in the lane
  But don't you rain on me.

2 Hey little April shower,
  Falling from the sky.
  Can't you stay there in that cloud?
  I just want to stay dry!
  You can rain on the rooftops in my street
  But don't you rain on me.

3 Hey little April shower,
  I am watching you.
  You are getting closer
  And soon I'll be wet through.
  You can rain and rain on my window pane
  But don't you rain on me.

4 Hey little April shower,
  Don't you rain on me.
  You can rain wherever you like
  But please stay clear of me.
  You can rain on the daffodils in the lane
  But don't you rain on me.

© 2009 Out of the Ark Ltd, Middlesex TW12 2HD
CCLI Song No. 5280748

HIP, HIP, HOORAY!
(WE'RE HAVING A HOLIDAY)

Words and Music by Mark and Helen Johnson

1   We've been working very hard every day,
    We're all ready for a rest. *(Teachers: Amen!)*
    Now's the time to have a holiday,
    And we will all come back refreshed!

    CHORUS   *Hip, hip, hooray! Hip, hip, hooray!*
             It's Easter time, we're having a holiday!
             Hip, hip, hooray! Hip, hip, hooray!
             It's Easter time, we're having a holiday!

2   No more nagging to be ready on time,
    No more rushing out of bed.
    No more 'Wakey, wakey! Rise and shine!'
    'Cause we can all relax instead!

    CHORUS

3   No more lessons for a couple of weeks,
    No more homework for a while. *(Yee hah!)*
    Won't be long till we can put up our feet
    And do the things that make us smile!

    CHORUS

4   Say 'Goodbye' to all your teachers and friends,
    Please remember all you've learned.
    Take good care until we meet again,
    And don't forget, come back next term!

    CHORUS

HOSANNA

Words and Music by Mark and Helen Johnson

1   Who spoke words of wisdom and life?
        Only the one they call Jesus.
    Understood what people are like?
        Nobody other than Him.
    Who performed miraculous signs?
        Only the one they call Jesus.
    Healed the sick, gave sight to the blind?
        Nobody other than Him.

	GROUP 1	GROUP 2
CHORUS	*Hosanna! Hosanna!*	*Rejoice!*
	Praise Him, come praise Him!	*Sing praise!*
	Hosanna! Hosanna!	*Rejoice!*
(BOTH)	*Lift up your voices and sing!*	

2   Who took children into his arms? *(Only the one, etc.)*
    Spoke to storms and made them be calm? *(Nobody other, etc.)*
    Who raised Lazarus up from the dead?
    Made a feast of fishes and bread?

    CHORUS

3   Who made friends with people despised?
    Turned the water into good wine?
    Who got people following Him?
    Changed their lives, forgave all their sin?

    CHORUS x 2

MARCH, APRIL, MAY

Words and Music by Mary Green and Julie Stanley

1   March is marching,
March is glad,
March is snowdrops,
March is mad!
March is nesting,
March is spring,
March shouts,
'Wake up everything!'

2   April's moody,
April's change,
April's sun,
April's rain.
April buds,
April flowers,
April sings
In April showers!

3   May is joyful,
May is bright!
May is blossom,
May is white.
May is fun,
May is play,
May's a promise
Of summer days!

MAY DAY DANCE

Words and Music by Jeff Hammer

1   Skip up and down,
     Dance round and round,
     With a long red ribbon in your hand,
     Skip, jump and hop,
     Dance and don't stop,
     To the sound of the music from the band.
     (Repeat)

     CHORUS   *Dance on May Day,*
               Dance on May Day,
               Dance on May Day,
               Around the maypole we go.
               (Repeat)

2   Skip in and out,
     Dance, laugh and shout
     As the ribbons wrap around the pole.
     Skip back again,
     Dance round your friend
     And watch as the ribbons unfold.
     (Repeat)

     CHORUS x 2

My Mum

Words and Music by Mark and Helen Johnson

1   My mum's one in a million,
    I'm sure that you would agree.
    I wouldn't say that she's perfect,
    But she's the best one for me.
    Sometimes she can get grumpy,
    And sometimes she gets upset,
    But I still know that she loves me,
    And that I'll never forget!

    CHORUS   *Oh! This is a Mother's Day song for you.*
    Mum, you're ever so special and I'm
    Gonna find ways to say I love you too!

2   My mum's ever so clever,
    She may not have a degree,
    But she can help with my homework
    And that's what matters to me.
    Sometimes she can be stressy,
    Sometimes even she shouts!
    But I still know that she loves me,
    And that's what certainly counts!

    CHORUS

3   My mum's really an angel,
    She's great at caring for me.
    She does the cleaning and shopping,
    And makes a wonderful tea!
    Sometimes she is too busy,
    Sometimes she is worn out,
    But I still know that she loves me,
    And that's what this is about!

    CHORUS x 2

    My mum's one in a million,
    I'm sure that you would agree.
    I wouldn't say that she's perfect,
    But she's the best one for me.

New Beginnings

Words and Music by Sha Armstrong

CHORUS   *It's time for new beginnings*
When cold dark days are at an end,
It's time for new beginnings
When spring is in the air and hope is everywhere,
Then it's time to live again.

1   To the seed that's buried in the earth,
To the seed playing dead,
To the seed that's buried in the earth,
Shout, 'WAKE UP, SLEEPY HEAD.'

CHORUS

2   To the egg that's lying in the nest,
To the egg playing dead,
To the egg that's lying in the nest,
Shout, 'WAKE UP, SLEEPY HEAD.'

CHORUS

3   To the hedgehog hidden in the leaves,
To the hedgehog playing dead,
To the hedgehog hidden in the leaves,
Shout, 'WAKE UP, SLEEPY HEAD.'

CHORUS   *It's time for new beginnings*
When cold dark days are at an end,
It's time for new beginnings
When spring is in the air and hope is everywhere,
Then it's time to live again,
Live again,
New beginnings, new beginnings.

PANCAKES

Words and Music by Mark and Helen Johnson

1   It's Shrove Tuesday, Pancake Day has come.
    Time for some cooking, time for having fun.
    We'll make some pancakes, lots for everyone.
    It's Shrove Tuesday, Pancake Day has come.

2   Making pancakes needs a careful plan,
    Eggs, milk and flour, butter and a pan.
    "Better roll your sleeves up, better wash your hands."
    Making pancakes needs a careful plan.

3   For the mixture, this is what you do:
    Blend the ingredients with a wooden spoon.
    Stir it round in circles till it's nice and smooth.
    For the mixture, this is what you do.

4   Heat some butter in a frying pan.
    Pour in the batter, cook it golden brown.
    Give the pan a jiggle, shake it all around.
    Now toss the pancake, … catch it if you can!
    Now toss the pancake, … catch it if you can!

Sing Out An Easter Song

Words and Music by Mark and Helen Johnson

CHORUS
Sing out an Easter song,
Tell everyone that the Lord has risen.
Sing out a joyful song,
Tell everybody that He's alive!

1 Jesus Christ, Son of God,
Gave His life upon a cross.
But the power of death was not
Enough to hold Him down.

CHORUS

2 Taken down from public view,
He was placed inside a tomb.
But the power of love broke through
And raised Him back to life!

CHORUS

3 He returned to see His friends,
Showed Himself alive again.
What a day it must have been
To have Him back again!

CHORUS x 2

SPRING CHICKEN

Words and Music by Mark and Helen Johnson

1   One mother hen sat on **4** little eggs,
Keeping them warm in her little egg nest.
Then one day she heard a crack
And a little voice said as the egg was hatched:

     CHORUS   *'I'm... a... spring chicken!*
I'm yellow and small.
My feathers are fluffy and they're keeping me warm.
My legs are not long so I'll never be tall,
But I'm a real spring chicken and I'm having a ball!
(Chicken, I'm a chicken, I'm a havin' a ball!)'

2   One mother hen sat on **3** little eggs,
Keeping them warm in her little egg nest.
Then one day she fell asleep
And a little voice said in a whispered tweet:

     CHORUS

3   One mother hen sat on **2** little eggs,
Keeping them warm in her little egg nest.
Then one day she moved about
And a little voice said as the chick popped out:

     CHORUS

4   One mother hen sat on **1** little egg,
Keeping it warm in her little egg nest.
Then one day she gave a sigh
And a little voice said, 'SURPRISE, SURPRISE!!'

     CHORUS x 2

SPRING FEVER!

Words and Music by Mary Green and Julie Stanley

There is something in the air,
I can feel it everywhere,
And you must feel it too!
Life is buzzin' all around,
Overhead and underground,
And the world is fresh and new,
It's spring in the air, out there for me and for you!

CHORUS   *It's that spring fever!*
                  It's that spring fever!
                  It's that spring fever!
                  It's spring fever getting to you!

Repeat verse

CHORUS x 2

Spring In My Toes

Words and Music by Niki Davies

1   I've got a spring, spring, spring in my toes,
I've got a spring, spring, spring in my toes.
I'm *skipping* along, singing a song,
I've got a spring in my toes.

2   I've got a spring, spring, spring in my toes,
I've got a spring, spring, spring in my toes.
I'm *hopping* along, singing a song,
I've got a spring in my toes.

3   I've got a spring, spring, spring in my toes,
I've got a spring, spring, spring in my toes.
I'm *jumping* along, singing a song,
I've got a spring in my toes.

4   INSTRUMENTAL

5   I've got a spring, spring, spring in my toes,
I've got a spring, spring, spring in my toes.
I'm *running* along, singing a song,
I've got a spring in my toes.

SPRING INTO ACTION

Words and Music by Sha Armstrong

CHORUS *Spring into action – winter has gone,*
Spring into action – summer come on,
The days are getting longer, the light is getting stronger,
Spring into action now.

1 Today it's time to sow the seeds
Now that spring is here,
Today it's time to sow the seeds,
It's my favourite season of the year…

CHORUS

2 Today it's time to clean the house
Now that spring is here,
Today it's time to clean the house,
It's my favourite season of the year…

CHORUS

3 Today it's time to play outside
Now that spring is here,
Today it's time to play outside
It's my favourite season of the year…

CHORUS *Spring into action – winter has gone,*
Spring into action – summer come on,
The days are getting longer, the light is getting stronger,
Spring into action now,
Spring into action now.

SUNSHINE, SHOWERS AND RAINBOWS

Words and Music by Matthew Crossey

1   Sunshine, showers and rainbows
All on the same day,
That's why I'm not quite sure what I'm wearing,
Or if the rain is here to stay.
It could be Wellington boots, a hat and a coat,
Gloves or my best shoes.
Sunshine, showers and rainbows,
That's why I don't know what to choose.

Sunshine and showers,
Sunshine and showers.

2   Sunshine, showers and rainbows
All on the same day,
That's why I'm not quite sure what I'm wearing
Or if the sun is here to stay.
It could be sun hat and shorts, a T-shirt or vest,
Or sandals for my shoes.
Sunshine, showers and rainbows
That's why I don't know what to choose.

Sunshine and showers,
Sunshine and showers,
Sunshine and showers.

SUPERMUM!

Words and Music by Ann Beresford

1 My mum's a
Story reading,
Baby feeding Supermum,
She's an all bed making,
Great cake baking Supermum.
She can hold three conversations whilst doing my sums,
She's a regular Supermum (oh yeah),
She's a wonderful Supermum!

CHORUS *Yes she's a*
Great, fantastic, love elastic Supermum,
She's a multi-tasking, well-worth asking Supermum,
She's got ears as well as eyes in the back of her head,
She's a regular Supermum (oh yeah),
She's my very own Supermum!

2 My mum's an
Eco-friendly,
All-recycling Supermum,
She's a lunch-box making,
Swimming taking Supermum.
She can hold three conversations whilst doing my sums,
She's a regular Supermum (oh yeah),
She's a wonderful Supermum!

CHORUS

3 My mum's a
Costume making,
School bag taking Supermum,
She's a fit fanatic,
Clear the attic Supermum.
She can hold three conversations whilst doing my sums,
She's a regular Supermum (oh yeah),
She's a wonderful Supermum!

CHORUS

THE APRIL SHOWERS

Words and Music by Sha Armstrong

CHORUS *The April showers are good for the flowers,*
They bring them back to life again,
So don't you worry, don't be in a hurry for the rain to end,
The showers are heaven sent.

1 The bluebells in the woods
Won't grow all by themselves,
The bluebells in the woods –
They need something else.

CHORUS

2 The daffodils in the park
Won't grow all by themselves,
The daffodils in the park –
They need something else.

CHORUS

3 The daisies in the grass
Won't grow all by themselves,
The daisies in the grass –
They need something else.

CHORUS

THE CHOCOLATE SONG

Words and Music by Mark and Helen Johnson

CHORUS *Oh I've got lots of chocolate,*
Give me lovely chocolate,
It's the best thing to eat, for sure.
When I get eggs for Easter
It's my favourite treat,
So I can always make some room for more!

1 I've got some plain and milk ones and some toffee-filled ones,
I've got boxes all around the place.
I've got a strong affection for my chocolate collection,
I'm mad about that chocolate taste!

CHORUS

2 I've eaten milky-white ones and the sweets inside them,
(I've got chocolate all round my face!)
They all had pretty wrappers, but that's not what matters,
I'm mad about that chocolate taste!

CHORUS

3 I've had some sickly sweet ones and some pretty cheap ones,
But I couldn't see them go to waste.
I s'pose I should know better, but it's nearly Easter,
I'm mad about that chocolate taste!

CHORUS x 2

THE POT OF CRESS

Words and Music by Mary Green and Julie Stanley

1 I've got a pot of compost,
 I've got a pack of seeds,
 Something has started growing,
 I hope it isn't weeds!

2 I've got a can of water,
 I've got a patch of sun,
 The shoots are getting taller and
 I've measured every one!

3 Look now my seeds are ready!
 I've grown a pot of cress –
 I've nibbled just a little bit,
 Mum can have the rest!

THE SEASON OF SINGING

Words and Music by Mark and Helen Johnson

1   It's quite a thing
    When the winter turns to spring,
    When the earth wakes up with colours
    So much brighter than we've seen.
    Everything around us is awakening,
    The season of singing is here.

2   It's quite a thing
    When you hear the call of spring,
    When the birds sit in the tree-tops
    And the world begins to sing.
    Everything around us is awakening,
    The season of singing is here.

    CHORUS   *Winter is gone,*
             There's a warmth in the sun,
             There's a fragrance upon the breeze.
             Open your eyes
             To the newness of life,
             Now it's everywhere to see.

3   It's quite a thing
    When the winter turns to spring,
    When the earth wakes up with colours
    So much brighter than we've seen.
    Everything around us is awakening,
    The season of singing is here.

    CHORUS

4   It's quite a thing
    When you hear the call of spring,
    When the birds sit in the tree-tops
    And the world begins to sing.
    Everything around us is awakening,
    The season of singing is here.
    The season of singing is here.

The Signs of the Time

Words and Music by Mary Green and Julie Stanley

1 The sun is in the sky
And the clouds are floating high,
Now the blackbird has built her nest.
The trees are turning green
And there's blossom to be seen,
Now the world is at its best –

These are the signs,
The signs of the time,
And the time is spring.

2 The daffodils are bright
And the tiny lambs are white
Now the robin has built her nest.
The hedgehog's awake
And the duck has found her drake,
Now the world is at its best –

These are the signs,
The signs of the time,
And the time is spring.

These are the signs,
The signs of the time,
And the time is spring.

Tick Tock
(The Clocks Go Forward)

Words and Music by Mark and Helen Johnson

A 60 second song, to be sung at 60 beats per minute!
(Sing as a round)

Start the clock!

A   Tick-tock, the winter has stopped
         So the clocks go forward, if you like it or not.

B   We'll be happy when the days are long,
         But we'll all be sleepy in the morning!

C   Don't forget to change your clock
         One whole hour, forward.

         Don't forget to change your clock!

WAKE UP!

Words and Music by Mark and Helen Johnson

CHORUS   *Wake up! Wake up!*
Give yourself a shake up,
Get your body moving.
Reach up, jump up,
Give your friend the 'thumbs up'!
It's another new day!
(Repeat)

Get your feet
Dancing to the beat,
Get your body moving.
Raise a shout (HEY!)
Let your feelings out,
It's another new day!

CHORUS

Repeat verse

INSTRUMENTAL

Get your feet
Dancing to the beat,
Get your body moving.
Raise a shout (HEY!)
Let your feelings out,
It's another new day!
(Repeat)

It's another new day!

WE'VE BEEN WAITING

Words and Music by Nikki Lewis

CHORUS *We've been waiting all through the winter,*
We've been waiting to say,
'No time to wait, today's the date,
It's too late to hibernate,
Get out of your bed you sleepy head,
Spring is here today!'

1   Sleepy dormouse, open your eyes,
Go on take a peep.
Get out of your bed you sleepy head,
Spring's no time to sleep!
Tortoise, don't hide under your shell,
Winter's in the past.
Get out of your bed you sleepy head,
Spring is here at last!

CHORUS

2   Hedgehog stretch your prickly back,
Don't curl into that ball.
Get out of your bed you sleepy head,
Spring is here for all!
Grizzly bear come out of your cave,
Growl 'hello' to the day.
Get out of your bed you sleepy head,
Spring is here to stay!

CHORUS

COPYRIGHT & LICENSING - What You Need To Know

The world of copyright and licensing can seem very daunting, particularly because there is an obligation on schools to comply with copyright law. We're here to help you through the process and to keep you legal. The guidelines below explain the most common copyright and licensing issues.

Singing Songs in the Classroom

You are free to use all of the material – including songs and scripts – in the classroom for teaching purposes. If photocopying any part of the book for teaching purposes please record this usage on your school's photocopy log to ensure that you are legally protected.

Singing Songs in an Assembly or in Church

Songs may be sung in assembly without charge. In addition, the CD may be played provided that your school has a PRS licence. However, the reproduction of the lyrics and/or musical scores for use in an assembly or a church requires a licence. The following licences from Christian Copyright Licensing Limited (www.ccli.com) permit the photocopying or reproduction of song lyrics or musical scores – for example to create song sheets, overhead transparencies or to display the lyrics or music using any electronic display medium:

For UK schools:　A Collective Worship Copyright Licence and a Music Reproduction Licence
For churches:　A Church Copyright and Music Reproduction Licence

The following credit should be included with the lyrics:

'Reproduced by kind permission © Out of the Ark Ltd'

Please ensure that you log the songs that are used on your CCLI and MRL copy report. Your CCLI licence also grants you permission to display the song lyrics from our Words on Screen™ CD ROMS on a whiteboard or other screen. Simply log the song titles on your copy report. Organisations that do not hold one of the above licences should contact Out of the Ark Limited directly for permission.

Singing Songs in a Concert

If you are performing any of our songs for the public on school premises (i.e. to anyone other than pupils or staff) then royalty payments become due. Contact Out of the Ark Music directly to obtain a licence. **Please note:** There is no need to obtain a licence from the publisher if your school has an arrangement with the **Performing Rights Society (PRS)** either directly or through the local authority.

If you are performing songs at a public venue (other than on the school premises or in a church) then the performance should be logged on the venue's PRS report.

The photocopying or reproduction of song lyrics or musical scores for use in concerts – for example to create song sheets, overhead transparencies or to display the lyrics or music using any electronic display medium – requires a licence. Please contact Out of the Ark Music directly.

Making an Audio Recording or a Video of the Performance

If you wish to make an audio or video recording of your performance of any of our works please visit **www.outoftheark.com/licensing** for further information.

Copying and File-sharing

Copying Out of the Ark Music's audio CDs is not permitted without obtaining a licence from the publisher. Installation of Out of the Ark Music's audio CD tracks on to a computer is strictly forbidden without a licence – we can provide schools with a 'Learning Platform Installation Licence'. File-sharing of any of our audio tracks or CD ROM files is strictly prohibited. For more information visit **www.outoftheark.com/licensing**.

Helpful information can be found on the following website:

A Guide to Licensing Copyright in Schools: www.outoftheark.com/licensing

And remember, we are always happy to help. For advice simply contact our customer services team:

Tel: +44 (0)20 8481 7200　　　　Email: copyright@outoftheark.com